American Women
of the
Space Age

MARY FINCH HOYT

American Women

of the

Space Age

ATHENEUM   *1966*   NEW YORK

FOR TOM AND STEVE

SONS WITH PATIENCE

American Women
of the
Space Age

CHAPTER

1

MAN HAS ALWAYS HAD AN UNQUENCHABLE SPARK OF curiosity about the nature of his world. Impelled to strike off in new directions, he has built roads across continents, charted hostile seas, and conquered the air in a flying machine. Each new adventure has given him a different perspective of his universe. And with this knowledge he has made a better way of life for himself.

No other effort to explore the unknown has been as dramatic as the spage age, heralded by the *beep-beep* of an artificial satellite placed into orbit by the Soviet Union on October 4, 1957. Suddenly there were roads to be built to the moon, virgin territory to be charted on other planets, and black areas to be explored between stars.

There was promise of more than adventure. The exploration of the moon promised to enrich our knowledge of what earth may have been like four and a half billion years ago. The clouds of Venus and the winds of Mars promised to advance the understanding of weather and climate. The new products derived from continuing space research, called the "spin-off" or "fall-out," portended a splendid future even for earth-bound men.

Sputnik hastened the commitment of the United States to a multi-billion dollars program. So the National Aeronautics and Space Administration (NASA) was established as a branch of the Federal Government to put scientists in universities to work on research, to direct research and development programs in industry, and to co-ordinate activities with the military forces and with the many foreign countries who wished to co-operate. The plan called for exploration of the solar system and outer space with manned and unmanned satellites and probes, and the application of space science and technology to human welfare. Within a very short time, an unprecedented surge of national energy was shifted to space research and development, turning it into the largest business in the world.

Members of the aerospace industry have been drawn from all professions and vocations: physicists, chemists, mathematicians, engineers, doctors, nurses, builders, technicians, artists, and designers. A great many are women, and from the beginning they have

4

played a varied and leading role.

For example, a woman mathematician tracking the unexpectedly erratic orbital variations of one of our first grapefruit-sized satellites perceived the fact that the earth might be not round but shaped like a pear.

At about the same time, a woman chemist, working on a team with five men, printed an entire electronic circuit on a thin ceramic wafer the size of a quarter, thereby making it possible to save priceless weight and space in rockets.

The development of the first rocket to stop and restart in space was co-ordinated by a woman engineer from Hollywood. Her ability to dovetail operations from the rocket's design through its fabrication, testing, assembly, and launch, led to her key position in aerospace management.

Women were called upon to help conceive ways to ensure the health, safety, and comfort of the first animals to be blasted from earth. A sculptress from Ohio, for example, molded a protective helmet for a chimpanzee, paving the way for human tests.

When finally man was placed into orbit, he carried with him special foods to be sampled for a female dietitian. Moreover, before and after the flight, he was cheered and tended by an Air Force launch-pad nurse.

As the program grew, so did the stature of the

women in it. Today, in unmanned scientific investigations in space, a former high school mathematics teacher directs NASA's sounding rocket program. An internationally known woman astronomer is chief of NASA's astronomy program, while another woman was partially responsible for the success of the first synchronous communications satellite to be "parked" in space, and now plans exotic spacecraft for future flights to other planets.

There are many thousands of men and women fitting pieces into the vast, complicated effort to master space.

Although it took at least 9,000 industrial and business organizations to launch the first man safely into space, many more of them will be required for his 239,000-mile trip to the moon. And the moon exploration itself, though it will be a triumph of man and machine never matched in history, will be just a beginning. Soon orbiting laboratories and space stations will be strung like a necklace of stepping stones into the heavens. Space buses will carry men and women to new planets: biologists, geologists, cartographers, engineers, military men, doctors, nurses, dietitians, and space scientists. They will chase comets, search for life, claim new territories, indeed, begin to *live* in other worlds.

But before this day, the boundaries of knowledge must be widened greatly. The limitations of the human body must be overcome. We are poised before a door-

6

way which may open onto indescribably wonderful answers to the problems of life and health: new raw materials, abundant foods, and exciting developments in electronics and weather control.

As in the past, the realization of such high adventure depends upon the spirit and inventiveness of the men and women who lead the way.

CHAPTER

2

THE TREMENDOUS SPEED IT TAKES TO SHOOT A MAN INTO space subjects his body to extremely "high G's," or a force of gravity many times that which holds him on earth. Later, when the speed of his vehicle counteracts the gravitational force of earth, there are "zero G's," or no pull at all, and he is weightless. Again, during re-entry through the earth's atmosphere, he must endure a gravitational force that for a moment makes him weigh more than half a ton. And so a space traveler's brain, nerves, organs, glands, and blood vessels must survive terrific stress one minute and adjust to a complete lack of it the next.

Learning how space travel will trigger the body's defense mechanism is the work of Dr. Evelyn Anderson, a gentle, soft-spoken doctor at the National Aeronautics and Space Administration's Ames Research Center in California. She is studying the pituitary and the hypothalamus — a small area of the brain connected with the pituitary. Basic information about the mechanisms of the hypothalamus and the pituitary will help doctors control man's reaction to new or frightening problems in space.

For many years before joining the space doctors, Evelyn Anderson specialized in endocrinology, the study of endocrine glands, which through the hormones they manufacture control most of man's involuntary bodily activities. At the National Institute of Health outside Washington, D. C., where she worked, she was experimenting with the brain to study its influence on the pituitary's function. She was also interested in the factors that cause the release of insulin into the blood — a related study. When the United States initiated its space program, she began thinking about ways in which her basic research would apply to the field of space medicine. How would the complex brain mechanisms control the endocrines during prolonged periods of weightlessness? When an astronaut became apprehensive in an abnormal atmosphere, how would his glands interact?

In 1962, increasingly intrigued by such questions, both Dr. Anderson (who uses her maiden name professionally) and her husband, Dr. Webb Haymaker, a

9

neurologist, moved to California to work with space scientists at Ames Research Center. Since that time her distinguished record in medical research and her contributions to space medicine have been recognized by the President of the United States, who chose her to receive a Federal Woman's Award in 1964.

What she and her colleagues are doing is developing a way to assay what may be called the "stress hormone" in blood. She has found that a neurohormone, made in the brain, is poured into the blood stream in large amounts when an individual is under stress. This hormone stimulates the release of the hormone ACTH.

Animals in a quiet, resting state do not have enough of this stress hormone to be detected, but when the animals are frightened or injured, large amounts of this stress hormone appear in the blood. Dr. Anderson uses this knowledge in order to study test pilots to determine how much stress they are under, and the effects on the human glandular system of such psychological and physical strains as acceleration and weightlessness.

In another laboratory, at Brooks Air Force Base in San Antonio, Texas, Dr. Jimmie Flume, a clever young female scientist, puzzles over the mystifying body processes that cause immunity from disease. She knows that the many microbes found in the body of every healthy man might multiply in lethal numbers if his resistance were lowered by weightlessness, radiation, or the other rigors of flight. Moreover, hypersensitivities or allergies might be aggravated by stress. And so to attack these problems, she studies cells, the most minute structures of life.

Dr. Flume studies cells by growing whole populations of them. Healthy tissue is taken from the body, fed with the proper amount of vitamins and minerals, and maintained with balanced acidity and alkalinity. In little glass vials, the living cells busily divide. With expert care, life can go on for long periods of time; even without food, cells can survive for as long as two weeks. And because these are laboratory-grown cells, free from the contaminators of an outside atmosphere, they are "pure." Therefore, their relative "health" and "sickness" can be studied easily both before and after space experiments.

To test their sturdiness after exposure to radiation, for example, Dr. Flume packaged several tubes of cells in Styrofoam, surrounded them with radiation dosimeters, and had them flown to California. The cells were launched and recovered with other space-born experiments. Then they were flown back to Dr. Flume's laboratory, where she examined them under the microscope, put them into a fresh medium, and prepared them for long-term observation to see what changes might develop.

Dr. Flume eventually hopes to clarify how certain

organisms strike body cells and cause them to build up resisting substances, or antibodies, which in turn cause immunity. This kind of research will help doctors to understand how man's body copes with disease both on earth and in outer space.

Jimmie Flume is a Texan by birth, who decided when she was a teenager to drop out of Incarnate Word College in San Antonio in order to be a hospital technician. But before she left, Sister Joseph Marie, a biologist, extracted a promise from Jimmie to return to her studies if the college built a new science hall. The hospital work stirred her interest in learning much more about living substance; and the college built a new science hall. So Jimmie returned to school, thereby taking steps which led to her space career. In spite of the fact that she has been dependent all her life on a crutch, she is a top space scientist as well as a lively young bride who manages her own home and garden and leads an active life outside her Air Force laboratory.

Pat Rydstrom is also searching for clues and solutions to questions involving the endurance of body cells. Her particular concern is in discovering what happens to living organisms after they have experienced sudden impact, spurts of great speed, periods of prolonged acceleration, heat, cold, vibration, and — of course — weightlessness.

She is advancing the techniques of histopathology.

Histology is a science named after the Greek word, *histos*, which means tissue, and *logos*, which means a discussion. Histology then deals with the examination of normal tissue under a microscope. Histopathology, on the other hand, is the study of the same tissues after they have been damaged.

Miss Rydstrom learned her research techniques early in life. She, too, thought that school was distasteful except when she was in biology classes. And then in her senior year in high school, her career was shaped by a veterinarian who let her assist in every phase of work in an animal hospital, giving her liberty to test her skills, allowing her to take charge, pointing out her errors in judgment.

When she started college, he helped her to fit her working hours to her study schedule. He taught her about blood counts, parasitological preparations and X-rays; about hospital and laboratory programing and maintenance. Chiefly, he taught her the value of paying attention to the smallest detail. He prepared her well to be a space researcher who studies animal tissue after it has been subjected to sudden stops and high speeds.

Another young woman in basic research in California is interested in high speed factors, too. She is Julie Beasely, who is an experimental psychologist at Ames Research Center. Miss Beasely experiments with laboratory animals to determine if periodic doses of "high G's" will change their behavior.

One of her psychological experiments is easy to understand. An animal is trained to press a bar a certain number of times, or after a certain interval of time, in order to get food. Miss Beasely works with him for two hours each day, teaching him that the only place he can get food is from an experimental tube. Then once a week he is put into a centrifuge — a motor-driven apparatus that rotates to produce five G's, or five times the force of gravity, for five hours, like a spacecraft. Immediately thereafter, the animal is tested to see if his performance in obtaining food from the tube is different than it was on any other day.

Elizabeth, "Betsy," Guild also endeavors to boost both the physical and psychological well-being of pilots and ground crews who may some day fly into space. Lieutenant Colonel Guild (rhymes with child) is an Air Force biological acoustician or one who studies the interaction of man and sound or noise.

On the night when she was born, Elizabeth Guild's father stayed up very late to finish writing a Ph.D. thesis which set the course for both their lives. He wrote about the effects of noise on hearing. Dr. Stacy Guild became one of the nation's leading authorities on the ear. And his daughter, Betsy, grew up to be an expert on the problems of space age noises produced by whining, screaming jet engines, rockets and missiles, spacecraft boosters and pumps, and supersonic airplanes.

Elizabeth Guild was always fascinated by her father's research on the structure and diseases of the ear. Immediately after she graduated from high school, she went to work in his laboratory at Johns Hopkins University, watching and listening, learning from him about the anatomy of the skull, the intricacies of the ear, and the techniques for giving hearing tests. Later, after she had earned an A.B. degree in clinical psychology at the University of Michigan, she joined a team of doctors at Johns Hopkins who were seeking ways to prevent hearing loss in young school children. And then World War II broke out.

She was in the first class of women to obtain officers' commissions when the Women's Army Auxiliary Corps (WAACS) was formed in 1942; a year later, she transferred to the WACS, the women's branch of the Army Air Corps. When peace was declared, she decided that there was clearly a special place in aviation medicine for one with her medical knowledge of hearing and Air Corps experience. At just about that same time, audiology — the study of hearing and noise — was suddenly acknowledged as important but neglected, and Betsy, now as a WAF (Women in the Air Force), began working in this new field of research.

The young Air Force officer's work was quite unique. It was her job to measure how much and what kind of noise and vibration was being generated in flight by engines, slip stream, radio sounds, or other factors. She then determined the effects of these noises on the hearing of the crews and on their ability to communicate with each other and with the ground. Her tasks were also to decide how well a man should hear to be physically qualified for his duties, and to ensure that he maintain his degree of hearing.

To do this, she helped design various forms of ear protectors and communication devices. Under her guidance, for instance, noise protective ear muffs were fabricated for the men who work on the ground beneath thunderous jet engines. These head sets and microphones are used today in very intense noise fields for communication from the ground to the cockpit while engines are being tested.

For people living near airfields, she has been developing techniques for minimizing disturbances. The sonic boom, for example — the noise caused by shock waves from supersonic airplanes — creates problems both near and far from air bases. Colonel Guild's research has included exposing herself to the most intense noises possible by standing directly beneath aircraft flying at supersonic speeds and as low as fifty feet. By proving that booms of this close range cannot hurt humans directly, she has helped to dispel the widespread worries about personal injury from sonic booms created by forthcoming supersonic transports.

Bigger, more powerful engines have magnified the

problems of noise. Not only does the noise level become higher in rocket engines and boosters and more powerful jet engines, but the pitch of the noise becomes lower and lower as the power increases. In their search for more information about this type of noise — which at a distance is more felt than heard — Colonel Guild and her colleagues in the Biological Acoustics Branch at Wright-Patterson AFB, Dayton, Ohio, have personally withstood intense noise down to one cycle per second (the ear does not hear until 20 c.p.s.). These are the kinds of experiments that are necessary for the health and performance of astronauts and ground crews of the space age.

CHAPTER

3

IN APRIL 1959, AT A PRESS PARTY IN WASHINGTON, D.C., seven carefully chosen young military pilots were introduced to the world as America's first space team. They had no idea what their exact role would be. All they knew was that a vast plan was being developed to launch men and machines into outer space; and they were to be the "astronauts" for the program which had been named "Project Mercury."

There was Navy Lieutenant Malcolm "Scott" Carpenter, 33; Captain Leroy "Gordo" Cooper, 32; Marine Lieutenant Colonel John Glenn, Jr., 37; Air Force Captain Virgil Grissom, 33; Navy Lieutenant Commander Walter Schirra Jr., 35; Navy Lieutenant Commander Alan Shepard Jr., 35; and Air Force

Captain Donald "Deke" Slayton, 35. They were all married, had children, and possessed above average intelligence. Moreover, they had been picked because they were stable, highly motivated, able to make decisions, and had volunteered to undergo unforeseen danger — even give up their lives. Literally nothing could be told to them about man in space or what it would take to get him there.

In the following four years, the astronauts learned to excel as space pilots, designers, engineers, and experimenters. They trained in the jungle, in the desert, and in the ocean. They studied astronomy. They exercised to keep in top physical shape. And they learned to maneuver in a prototype spacecraft the size of a telephone booth. Finally, with the help of more than two million other Americans, they awed the world with six suspenseful flights, accumulating fifty-three and one-fourth hours in outer space, at a cost of more than ten million dollars an hour. Project Mercury was a success.

Many worked behind the scenes involved in a new profession that they called "life support," meaning in the broad sense that their job was to help man adjust comfortably to his new experience by developing a safe, familiar environment for him as well as other essentials such as suitable clothing and food.

One woman in life support research, Beatrice Finkelstein, a nutritionist, was convinced that eating

19

three delicious meals a day would save a spaceman from boredom, irritability, mistakes, and possible disaster. She became the dietitian for the Mercury astronauts, turning her talents toward research into food for space that would provide nourishment, be anticipated and savored, and supply a lift to the spirits.

Bea Finkelstein began thinking seriously about the importance of good nutrition when she was in college. Influenced by an older sister who was studying medicine, she took courses in physiology, public health, and chemistry. Then one summer she volunteered to catalog some 2,000 foreign and American cookbooks for her physiology teacher. When she graduated from college, that same professor recommended her for a research fellowship in nutrition at Columbia University.

After several years of graduate study and teaching, she went to work for the U. S. Air Force as a civilian. Her responsibility was to sit on the "master menu board" that evaluated the food programs for the armed services. She also met with Air Force doctors to formulate flight feeding plans and nutritional requirements for pilots all over the world. She loved her new work, which took her to places like Thule, Rabat, Casa Blanca, Goose Bay, and Germany. Then in 1956, when Air Force doctors and psychologists in Dayton, Ohio started wondering how man would actually function in space, they turned to her for her special knowledge of nutrition. She joined them in an "aeromedical" laboratory in Dayton — her office was a sparkling rose-pink kitchen — and began to help devise the tests necessary to determine what was needed for space feeding.

Her first tests on human subjects showed, among other things, that, when men were locked up in an artificial spacecraft with a loaded refrigerator, the eating area became their center of activity. Food turned out to be intensely significant for those "on board." They bartered their rations like precious jewels.

It was also found that when subjects were confined alone in total darkness, foods tasted alike and were not as good. A ham on rye bread sandwich tasted just like chicken on white bread. Even for those with a sweet tooth, brownies lacked flavor. Some men opened the refrigerator door at five minute intervals, or became angry and refused to eat. Clearly, food was an important "tool" for man.

Although Bea Finkelstein and her fellow researchers gained new information about how individuals act in unfamiliar isolation, one big problem remained: even if he were hungry and happy, would a spaceman be able to chew, swallow, and digest in weightlessness? Would food make him space sick? And how could his meals be packaged for zero gravity where everything is weightless and a knife, fork, spoon, or a drop of gravy, might float around dangerously inside a spacecraft?

Miss Finkelstein went to work in her kitchen, experimenting with cold, thin, high-protein liquids that could be forced down the gullet from the kind of collapsible plastic tube that is used for many things today. Volunteers were enlisted to try her toothpaste-tube concoctions. Surprisingly, by the end of a very few days, most of the men grew to like strange blends of strained meat and concentrated ice cream mix. Some of the subjects stated that they had never felt better in their lives.

As Project Mercury progressed, the astronauts themselves started testing space menus in what they called "Bea's Diner." They were going to need a special bland, low-residual diet — much the same as the hospital fare given to patients before surgery — for at least seventy-two hours before they were launched. Bea experimented for them: she used variety and imagination, seasoning portions of purée of pea with oregano, sprinkling purée of tomato with rosemary and thyme. Her special diet baked breast of chicken prompted one astronaut's wife to complain that she was no longer hearing about "Mother's cooking" but about "the way Bea fixes it."

When at last the first orbital space flight was scheduled in January 1962, she flew to Cape Kennedy, which was then called Cape Canaveral, to be with the Mercury astronauts.

Marine Colonel John Glenn, in peak physical and mental condition, had been picked for the job and flight had been scheduled for January 27. But on that day, ominous clouds hung over the Cape. Nevertheless,

Glenn rose, ate his special breakfast, took a pre-flight physical examination, and rode to the launch pad where his spacecraft, Friendship 7, rested like a dark bell on top of its rocket.

For eight hours he remained there, confined inside the craft, waiting for the weather to clear. Across the nation, in homes, schools, and offices, radios and television sets were tuned to Florida. Then, only thirteen minutes before launch, the flight was "scrubbed," or canceled. Disappointment swept the country, but Glenn emerged from his capsule, grinning. "Well," he said, "back to Bea's diet."

Twenty-four days later, on February 20, 1962, John Glenn was successfully placed into orbit around the earth. High over Kano, Nigeria, he ate the first home-cooked American meal in outer space. Bea had prepared beef, vegetables, and apple sauce for him. But as he later said, "On the relatively short flight of Friendship 7, eating was not a necessity, but rather an attempt to determine whether there would be any problem in consuming and digesting food in a weightless state. At no time did I have any difficulty eating. I believe that any type of food can be eaten as long as it does not come apart easily or make crumbs."

A little over a year later on the fourth and last Project Mercury flight, astronaut Gordon Cooper attempted to eat a perfectly normal lunch in space. Crumbs were indeed a problem. On the fifth pass around the earth, Cooper radioed the following message: "Now I'm preparing to eat a little bite. The sandwiches that I am looking at here are pretty crumbly, lot of crumbs floating all over in the bag that they're in. I may not open them." He didn't. A few minutes later he reported having eaten small cakes and bacon with some sips of water.

By the end of Project Mercury, it was evident that man could eat quite normally for short periods of time in a weightless state. But Bea Finkelstein and other food researchers wanted to know what type and amount of food could be loaded into a spacecraft for a trip lasting weeks, months, or possibly years. Meals have to be planned to taste good, weigh little, and take up minimum space.

Until long interplanetary travel makes it necessary to abandon fairly conventional diets, scientists are working to make the space menu as familiar as an ordinary picnic lunch. The food, however, will be served in collapsible containers, or in bite-size biscuits coated with a thin, tasteless film to prevent crumbling. Hot and cold meals that can be prepared in and eaten from the containers in which they are packed will be developed. Soups and juices will be stored in squeeze bottles.

To promote interest in trading food, special individual rations will be planned for each person in a crew. The space galley will be designed with a refrigerator and a freezer just like those in a kitchen on earth.

For trips of longer duration, freeze-dried food will be packaged in special feeding devices into which a tube can be inserted and water added so that the astronaut can "reconstitute" his meals. Later, scientists believe that "slurry" — a watery mixture of amino acids, metabolites, and vitamins — might be acceptable. Or algae, the microscopic plant life that consumes carbon dioxide and liberates oxygen, might be used as a source of food and serve at the same time to "air condition" spacecraft. But until his normal eating habits are changed drastically, the food to which the space traveler is accustomed on earth may be a vital link with normality when he is hurtling toward the stars.

During Project Mercury, food was also an important ingredient in the survival kits packed for the astronauts in case they landed in remote areas where they could not be rescued easily. Scott Carpenter, for example, waited in the sea for three hours before he was picked up. In his case there was no reason for fear. As a matter of fact his account of these hours sounds almost as if he was holding a party. "Soon there were a lot of airplanes around, but I just sat there minding my own business. Suddenly, I heard a voice calling from behind me. I turned around and there was someone swimming up to me. I did not even know that he had been parachuted into the water. He inflated his raft, climbed in, and attached his raft to mine . . . later, another swimmer joined us. I broke out the food and asked them if they wanted any; but they had finished lunch recently, and they did not take any."

Carpenter was prepared, of course, for a stay of much longer than three hours, and there were many things in addition to food in his survival kit. The kit had been designed and fabricated by a young woman named Rita Rapp. She had helped perfect, for example, an automatic hypodermic needle for pain, which Carpenter could have shot like a firing pin through his space suit, into his leg.

Waiting at the Cape, another young woman prepared to minister to his needs. She was Dee O'Hara, an Air Force Lieutenant who became the "world's first space nurse." Lieutenant O'Hara's duties included maintaining the astronauts' eight-room medical facility on the Cape and helping the flight physician to maintain the physical well-being of the young men throughout each mission.

Lieutenant O'Hara was the first of many. Large numbers of space nurses will be required to care for future pilots, scientists, maintenance men, and others who venture into space and stay there. And there are many questions that need answers. For example, how can a nurse bathe and tend a patient when both are

1. Dr. Evelyn Anderson, endocrinologist, works in the field of space medicine.
NASA photo, Ames Research Center

2. Alice Chatham, who works on the development of space suits and helmets and other comforts, created this "space bed."

3A. Dorothy B. John, a mathematician, checking the information put into a digital differential analyzer.
Air Force photo, Wright-Patterson AFB, Ohio

3B. Lee Curry Rock with an inflated space suit. She helps develop protective coverings for spacemen.
Air Force photo, Wright-Patterson AFB, Ohio

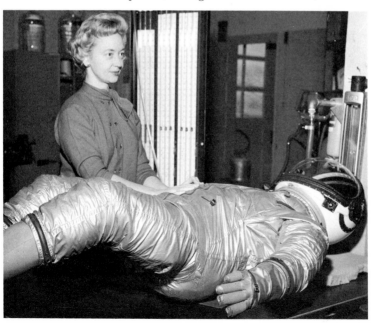

4. Julie Beasely, an experimental psychologist, studies the effects of high forces of gravity on animal behavior. *NASA photo, Ames Research Center*

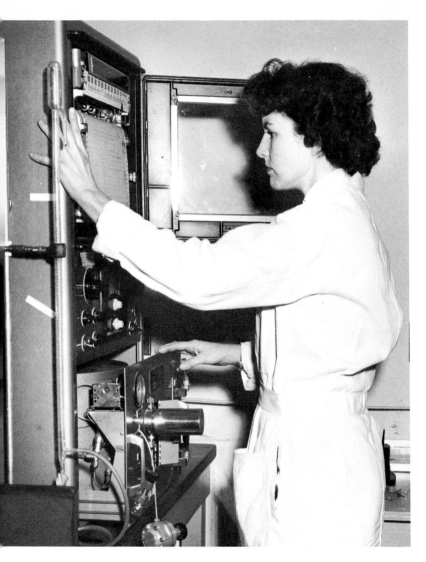

5. Merna Dawson analyzes fuels and knows how they react in space-like conditions.

6. Bea Finkelstein working on the problems of food for spacemen.

7. Lieutenant Colonel Elizabeth Guild is concerned with the extreme noise given off by spacecraft, and devises methods of protection against it.

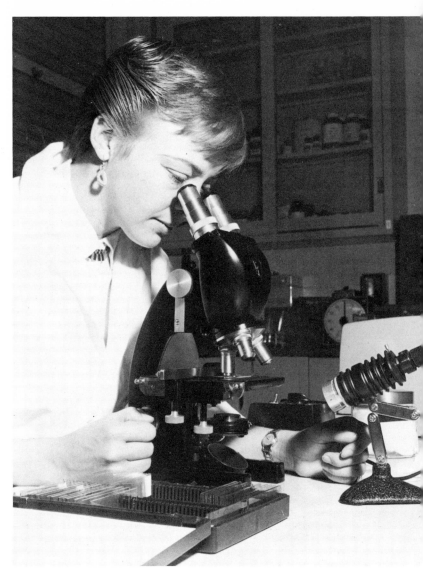

8. Pat Rydstrom studies the effects of conditions
in space on living cells. *Northrop Corporation*

attired in space suits and in a situation of weightlessness? How will a dehydrated patient be given fluids intravenously when his veins are weightless? And what good will it do to elevate the feet of a person in shock when the blood will not rush down to his head?

Preparing meals, performing daily nursing tasks; these means of supporting man will probably continue to be mainly woman's work on earth and in outer space.

CHAPTER

4

AFTER PROJECT MERCURY, GEMINI, THE SECOND STAGE of the United States manned space flight program, was designed to give the astronauts a chance to experiment for longer periods of time in strange, simulated, or artificial surroundings.

Gemini astronauts, named for the zodiacal twins, traveled in pairs. They were sealed in spacecraft that looked much like the earlier, simpler Mercury capsules. But the Gemini missions were far more complex.

Now it was time to learn to control spacecraft during orbit and re-entry. Rendezvous and docking experiments were important. They would make it possible for spacecraft to meet and join in space, thereby enabling man to move about freely. There was still much to find out about the physical and mental reactions of men to weeks or months of weightlessness, confinement, and isolation. And before spaceships could be repaired, or other satellites inspected and serviced, or food transferred from one place to another, men had to learn to perform chores while floating free in space in what was called "extravehicular activity" (EVA).

America's first EVA mission was a stunning success. On June 3, 1965, Gemini astronaut Major Edward H. White II, about 120 miles above the earth, climbed out of the hatch of his spacecraft and propelled himself into the sky. For twenty-two minutes he maneuvered in outer space, equipped with his own rocket power and oxygen supply, secured to his craft only by a twenty-four foot, gold-colored "umbilical" cord. Inside the spaceship, his fellow pilot, Major James McDivitt, described the feat to fifty million Americans who were listening on radio and TV. Among them were several women who had a particular interest in the accomplishment.

Margaret Jackson, a quiet, blonde woman, works in NASA's 1,620-acre Manned Spacecraft Center in Houston, Texas, where Major White's walk was being monitored. An environmental physiologist, she is concerned with man's need to breathe his own peculiar gaseous atmosphere. This envelope of air, surrounding earth, is mainly composed of oxygen and nitrogen; it is vastly different from the near vacuum of space. Although it is the oxygen man needs, pure oxygen is too rich for him to absorb over an extended period of time. In fact, breathing pure oxygen would be fatal after about two weeks. And so man must take a mixture of familiar gases with him in order to survive. Moreover, the humidity and temperature of his air must be regulated so that, for instance, moisture won't build up inside his space suit in the freezing temperatures of the moon, or heat won't build up inside his suit to a dangerous level.

Miss Jackson and her colleagues in NASA's Crew Systems Division are studying "life support" requirements by testing the reactions of human subjects to different gases, temperatures, and pressures. For some time this was done on equipment that looked more like scrap in an inventor's basement than sophisticated laboratory machinery.

In one test, Miss Jackson connects a space-dressed human subject to a device that combines a conglomeration of gasometers, cardiographs, EEG equipment and other testing apparatus. Then the subject walks at a predetermined rate on a treadmill; the expired gases from his lungs are collected periodically and are then analyzed. From these findings, physiologists can chart the effects on man's blood pressure, heart action, body temperature and metabolism when he is working or resting under space-like atmospheric conditions.

She and other scientists are aware of the need to maintain a constant earth-like atmosphere in space-ships, where storage is not possible. One method may be to capture, purify, and re-use the space man's breath.

Perhaps scientists will use fast-growing algae to help keep the air usable; these will thrive on expired breath gases, sunlight, urine, and excrement and, in turn, renew oxygen, purify wastes, and produce high protein food. Or, it might be more feasible to supply oxygen by electrolysis, which uses an electrical current to break down water into its oxygen and hydro-gen components.

Margaret Jackson became interested in space flight in 1941 when she joined the Aero Medical Labo-ratory in Wright Field, Ohio, to assist in simulated high altitude studies. As a part of her job, she became the first woman to "free float" in zero-G, or weightlessness. Air Force pilots were simulat-ing weightlessness for short periods of time in aircraft that roller-coasted fast enough to change the pull of gravity from 2.5 to zero. Experiments under this space-like condition were being conducted in the padded, barn-like cabin of an Air Force C131-B aircraft. Eager to experience the odd sensation, Miss Jackson agreed to dress in flight suit and helmet and accompany other subjects on an experimental flight.

She said afterward: "It was fascinating. One feels

completely buoyant. Like floating on sea water, only completely free." Since that time, astronauts have proved that weightlessness, sometimes called "rapture of the deep," is so pleasant that it is hard to force oneself to return to normal. But scientists warn that prolonged periods in this agreeable state may soften bones and cause heart and artery fiber to lose elasticity.

When Major White floated, weightless, outside his spacecraft, he was totally encased in a pressurized space garment with a special inlet at his waist through which air was fed from the craft, for breathing and ventilation. His twenty-one-layered nylon, mylar and felt suit, which weighed 31½ lb. on earth, had been developed after extensive research in government and industrial laboratories where scientists and engineers constantly try to add to their knowledge of space necessities.

Lee Curry Rock conducts this kind of research. She works at the Aerospace Medical Research Laboratory at Wright-Patterson Air Force Base. Young Mrs. Rock is an engineer, and a relative newcomer to the fields of physiology and space protective equipment, who helps develop and test protective coverings for space personnel.

She hopes to make space clothing functional so that man can move about comfortably in heat and cold and remain, at the same time, safe from such hazards as meteorites or solar flares. During this time, traveling in the near vacuum of space, man must be surrounded by a minimum pressure of 3.5 lb. per square inch or his body liquids will expand, become gaseous, and fatally rupture his body cells.

Life-sustaining pressure in a vacuum can be provided pneumatically or mechanically. A space garment with pneumatic protection is like a balloon of gas under pressure encasing the body. Mechanical protection, on the other hand, can be provided in the form of fabric or material that will tighten against the skin automatically. Mrs. Rock is testing fabrics on human-form dummies to find a method of providing this mechanical pressure in extravehicular space suits.

She is also searching for new "fog-resistant" coatings for space helmet visors that will keep droplets of perspiration from clouding the spaceman's vision. Of the means now under study, one involves heating the visors electrically, which sometimes produces too much heat for comfort, another spraying a dry gas over the visor to pick up the moisture, another applying a film of household detergent that causes the droplets to form a clear film over the visor. But a more durable, less fragile coating is needed.

Curiously, back in 1942, at the Aerospace Medical Research Laboratory, another woman started on a space career that also advanced the development of suits and helmets. At that time scientists were being mobilized to contend with the problems of World War II, and they asked Alice Chatham, then Alice King, a well-known sculptor in Dayton, Ohio, to pool her talents with them. Specifically, Air Force scientists wanted to draw on her knowledge of anatomy and design to help develop pressurized oxygen-breathing masks for fighter pilots. And so she began to help model and fabricate leak-proof rubber masks that fit tightly over the mouth and nose of a pilot needing extra oxygen when flying at high altitudes.

Soon she was assigned a project of her own: to design a special helmet to be worn with a partial pressure suit that would pressurize a man's face and ears. The project was urgent because the first rocket plane, the X-1, was nearly ready to be tested. Only creating an artificial environment to protect the pilot in the event of cabin pressure failure would make it safe for him to fly.

The final test of the finished model was harrowing for all concerned. A young doctor, who was a friend of Mrs. Chatham, volunteered to test it out. Dressed in a partial pressure suit, with the test helmet on his head, he was to determine its strength and durability in a chamber under pressure so great that he would die instantly if anything went wrong. Mrs. Chatham's helmet fortunately proved safe and strong at pressures equal to an altitude of 100,000 feet.

Now the way was paved for Captain "Chuck"

Yeager to break the sound barrier or fly faster than the speed of sound. For his historic flight in October, 1947, he wore a similar helmet, which Mrs. Chatham had carefully made by hand. This early partial pressure helmet had a full-face rubber mask attached to a cloth hood, which hugged the head and neck. The mask was pressurized by means of an inflatable, rubber face-sealing bladder, which included the ears. A separate hard hat was placed over the cloth headpiece for buffeting protection, which was badly needed in the first rocket planes. In contrast to this relatively crude device, in 1965, Gemini pilot White wore a plastic helmet off which bullets could be bounced. Thirty times stronger than the canopy of an airplane, it had two visors to protect him from micro-meteorites and the sun's raw glare in outer space.

Breaking the sound barrier opened the corridor for space missions. As supersonic vehicles lifted man closer to the earth's "limb", or the edges of its atmosphere, scientists began testing more animals in flight research to prepare for man's journey into orbit. Alice Chatham was asked to design a special protective sack for a rhesus monkey who was to be wind-blasted at 700 miles per hour. She set about designing, instead, a tough little airworthy suit and a miniature protective helmet. She worked while the monkey was anesthetized, cutting the suit pattern in navy blue nylon, molding the tiny, full-head helmet, with a fiberglass shell and

35

a clear plastic face-piece. (One evening she sewed Sergeant's stripes on the sleeve of the suit.) The monkey survived the test in good health in his space outfit and, months later, Mrs. Chatham used it as a pattern for similar ones for "Project Whoosh" chimpanzees who were ejected from airplanes at speeds faster than sound.

When the first living animal, another rhesus monkey, was successfully lofted thirty-four miles into space in an Aerobee rocket, he wore a restraining harness and a special mask that Mrs. Chatham had created. She also packaged the monkey in a harness with foam rubber padding to keep his bones from rubbing against the capsule.

For "Major," a 140 lb. St. Bernard dog, who tested early automatic devices for opening parachutes, she designed a suit to shield him from the cold. Heavy strips the length of his back protected his spine against the opening shock of the parachute, which occurred when he was released from an airplane bomb bay to drop, safely, 26,000 feet to earth.

She also contributed to Project "Sierra Sam" by casting a paper test-dummy of a 200 lb. Air Force major. From this paper cast, an original model was made. The distribution of weight of the dummy was proportionate to that of a man, which made it invaluable in experiments to help discover what would happen if a pilot was ejected from his craft while air-borne.

In 1954, twelve years after she had exchanged her

art studio for the research laboratory, she moved to California and became one of the first non-scientifically trained women to be directly involved in the manned space flight program. One of her very first jobs was to cast the heads of the original seven Mercury astronauts in wax so that perfect linings could be fitted inside their protective helmets.

Alice Chatham's innovations have appeared in a variety of experimental orbiting laboratories in which "null gravity" studies are being performed, at Douglas Aircraft Company in Santa Monica, California. For a space cabin simulator, for instance, she designed a "space bed" and, for its occupants, comfortable, stretch-knit garments whose materials and design meet the rigid requirements of space. These are "constant-wear," day and night garments that serve a dual purpose: they can be used as undergarments when their wearers have to don pressure suits quickly in an emergency.

She has also designed different kinds of restraints and tethering devices — similar to the umbilical cords used by Gemini astronauts. And for space technicians of the future who might need to hang inside booster tanks in space in order to repair them, she has produced overalls of stretchy, fish-net fabric that will allow the men to work comfortably.

Mrs. Chatham and laboratory scientists are constantly improving designs for orbiting laboratories and other future spacecraft. Some day in a belt of whirling

37

space stations, man's ability to live in space will be determined; the eroding effects of a space atmosphere on electronic instruments, fluids, lubricants, metals, and other structural materials will be watched; stars will be studied without the interference of earth's atmosphere; and new experiments in geodesy, the biosciences, and other fields will be conducted. The space stations will orbit for long periods of time and will be re-supplied by rocket ships. Although crews will be exchanged, some personnel will be semi-permanent. This being the case, many things will have to be designed to keep them comfortable, safe, and happy.

CHAPTER

5

THE SURFACE OF THE PLANET EARTH, WHICH IS gradually but constantly eroded by friction from the atmosphere, washed by oceans, and convulsed by the activity of shifting mountains, is vastly different today from what it was several hundred million years ago when the solar system was formed. But the earth's satellite, the moon, comparatively quiet and serene, is probably much the same as it was. And so, mapping, surveying, and exploring the moon's physical features holds promise for scientists who wish to unlock the secrets of our universe.

The National Aeronautics and Space Administration's third manned space program, Project Apollo, named for the Greek sun-god, was planned to give man this opportunity. Apollo calls for launching forty-five tons of man and machine toward the moon. Three astronauts will go first. Their craft will have a command center, in which they will sit side by side, a service unit for fuel and power, and a weird, spiderish "lunar excursion module," called a LEM, which will utilize rocket power for a slow, safe, or "soft" landing on the moon.

Here the "rendezvous" and "docking" experience of Project Gemini will be important, for while one astronaut in the command module will circle in lunar orbit, the other members of the Apollo team will separate in the LEM and land on the moon's dusty, scarred landscape. They will plant instruments on the lunar surface that will send data back to earth about the moon's structure and the characteristics of its atmosphere, heat flow, solar wind, and radiation. Then the bug will rendezvous with its mother ship and return to earth.

After Apollo, man will build lunar bases from which he can set out for Venus (a five month trip) and Mars (an eight month trip); and one day, perhaps, for Mercury, Jupiter, Saturn, Uranus, Neptune, and Pluto. The limits of such adventure, however, will depend upon his ability to harness power and fuel for rocket boosters, improve launch vehicles, sub-systems and spacecraft, and perfect guidance systems that will lead the way back home. In brief, scientists must learn more and more about the basic essentials of powered flight.

Early in the twentieth century, in 1903, the brothers Orville and Wilbur Wright astonished the world by flying 120 feet, staying aloft for twelve seconds in a flimsy-winged box propelled by a twelve horse-power engine that they built in their basement. The Wright brothers had air for a working fluid, and the oxygen in the atmosphere, combined with the fuel in their engine, carried them over the sand dunes at Kitty Hawk. But this type of engine, of course, could not function in the vacuum of outer space.

Only twenty-three years later, in 1926, Dr. Robert H. Goddard, an American physicist, launched a toy-sized, liquid fuel rocket that was to liberate man from the confines of earth. Although it lifted only a few feet into the air, it did not require oxygen from the atmosphere to propel it. The space age had truly begun.

Soon, more sophisticated rockets were conceived to shove objects through the atmosphere, high into outer space, and bring them back intact by braking the speed of their descent. As a matter of fact, it took less than forty years to design the gargantuan Saturn V rocket for Project Apollo. A mighty, three-stage, power-house, Saturn weighs about 3,000 tons, operates elec-tronically, and will move at about 24,200 miles per hour as it travels the distance of 239,000 miles to the moon. Helping to make all this possible were many men — and women.

Edith Olson, for instance, a civilian chemist with the United States Army in Washington, D.C., helped to shrink the electronic parts of rockets down to paper-thin, thumb-nail size, thus saving critical weight and space. (A 1 lb. reduction in equipment saves 5 - 7 lb. of fuel, lightens a rocket's load, and allows it to go farther.)

Mrs. Olson is an inorganic chemist. She chose this field because, as a young girl, her family had urged her to examine stones and bugs and water under a microscope. After receiving a college degree, the young chemist went to work at the Bureau of Standards, hoping to find new ways to use chemical compounds in space-age rockets.

Mrs. Olson and a team of four other Army scientists set about developing a method of "printing" entire electronic systems with chemicals on tiny ceramic wafers. They combined the techniques of photography and lithography, "baking on" layers of conductors and resistors made of silverish paint and a compound that looked like black mayonnaise. The fine, pin-dot work had to be done under the lens of a microscope. When finished, more than a half dozen of the miniature, two-dimensional wafers could fit into the palm of Mrs. Olson's hand. Moreover, they allowed scientists to pack five times more electronic gear into space equipment.

This development was a boon to both rocket engineers and electronic inventors looking for smaller, more durable, less fragile and cheaper parts for computers, TV sets, hearing aids and the like. For her contribution, Mrs. Olson was the first woman ever to receive the Department of Defense's highest cash award. She and her teamworkers, whose new concept was estimated to save 200 million dollars a year for the space effort, shared a 25,000 dollar prize awarded them by the Secretary of the Army in 1959.

"It's like printing all the works in the Library of Congress on a grain of rice," she said at the time. "We work on the theory that electronic equipment in the future will be too big if you can see it."

This forecast was highly accurate. Today, drafting boards in industry and government laboratories call for a whole new array of doll-sized objects: AM radios that will fit into finger rings; TV sets, with tubes flat as pancakes, that can be hung onto walls like pictures; "radio pills," containing complete power and transmitting stations in tiny, gelatin capsules, that can be swallowed by patients to "broadcast" their internal problems to doctors; thimble-sized computers; and, of course, electrical components so small that complete emergency, or "back up" sets of duplicate, miniature power systems can be carried in modern spacecraft and missiles and rockets.

Other teams of chemists, including several young women in California, are searching for and testing out new concepts in space-power technology. Merna Dawson is one of them. She is an analytical chemist in aeronautical fuels at the Edwards Air Force Base Rocket Site — a gleaming, white laboratory on top of a mountain that rims the flat, shimmery, dry Muroc lake bed which lies about seventy-five miles away from Los Angeles.

This is the home of the X-15 and other exotic experimental vehicles that fly far into space. Overhead, in the clear blue desert sky, the planes look like bats, Coca-Cola bottles, and huge, ungainly pears. The sleek, supersonic X-15 rocket ship, for example, which is dropped from a B-52 mother ship to study man's flight through the earth's atmosphere, flies faster than 4,000 miles per hour and can reach an altitude of more than sixty miles.

Miss Dawson's job is to analyze and evaluate proposed propellants for the X-15 and the other craft to determine whether or not they are suitable and safe. For example, she runs tests in her chemistry laboratory to find out if the structural materials used in the crafts' fuel systems are "compatible" with new liquid and solid fuels about to be tested. Testing these fuels in supersonic and hypersonic planes is one way to find out how they will react in conditions that are like space flight.

44

The aerodynamic performances of the strange-shaped flying objects at Edwards AFB are constantly recorded, assayed, and improved. Similarly, new sizes and shapes for lunar ships and interplanetary probes are tried out at Ames Research Center at Moffett Field, California. In this NASA laboratory, Barbara Short, an aerospace engineer, is observing and recording the aerodynamic stability of spacecraft shapes by taking pictures of tiny, jewel-sized, scale models that are shot out of a gun-like device.

Miss Short, who plays bridge and bowls in what few hours of spare time she can find, started testing the shape of the Project Mercury capsule back in 1959. Using a tiny pellet no larger than the charm on a bracelet, an exact replica 1/165th the size of the capsule, and accurate to within .0005 of an inch, she shot it and followed its flight through a "free flight" ballistic range to see how it would fall through the air. If fired off center, could it straighten up and fly properly? Would a real spacecraft of the same shape, re-entering the earth's atmosphere at 18,000 miles per hour, burn itself up from friction?

The flights were staged in a huge metal tunnel. As the toy spacecraft sped through the air, electric beams on the sides of the tunnel tripped cameras that took "shadowgraphs," or profiles of the capsule's various positions in flight as it passed by. The film of each flight and the record of the time it took each

45

capsule to fly between stations were evaluated by engineers who modified the spacecraft until they were finally certain what its precise trajectory, or path, would be.

The actual Mercury spacecraft in which John Glenn rode around the earth was a bell-shaped structure about six feet wide at the bottom and about nine feet long. The re-entry module of the Gemini spacecraft, whose air-worthiness was also checked and re-checked by Barbara Short, was similar in shape but larger, measuring about seven feet wide at the bottom and almost eleven feet long. For spacecraft that were designed to fly at lightning speed this may seem like a funny, awkward shape. But the wide-bottomed, or blunt capsules were adopted after a revolutionary discovery, quite by accident, in free flight tests at Ames in 1952.

At that time, Mr. Julian Allen, the Director of Ames Research Center, for whom Barbara Short worked, fired a cylinder-shaped slug down the range and found on the "shadowgraph" that strong shock waves preceded the little object. In later tests it was shown that a similarly shaped, blunt-nosed spacecraft would create wide shock waves that would dissipate the enormous heat built up by the friction of the atmosphere on re-entry from space. This concept was one of the major discoveries in early space age research.

46

CHAPTER

6

IN THE ARDENT, NEVER-ENDING QUEST TO FIND OUT MORE about the cosmos, astronomers, physicists, biologists, and scientists in many other disciplines, launch instruments into the heavens to record unexplained or unknown phenomena in space. Some mount their experiments in "sounding rockets," relatively small, up-and-down rockets that fly through the atmosphere and then fall back to earth. Others collect data from orbiting satellites, craft of different sizes and shapes that are launched into orbit around the earth.

The National Aeronautics and Space Administration executives, Miss Eleanor Pressly and Dr. Nancy Grace Roman, supervise important and entirely different aspects of these scientific investigations. Miss

Pressly, a former mathematics teacher, meshes all operations for a sounding rocket program. Dr. Roman, a distinguished astronomer, is in charge of scientific astronomy experiments, which are often flown in orbiting satellites. For their uncommon achievements in space work, each has received the Federal Woman's Award from the President of the United States.

Eleanor Pressly, who grew up in Due West, South Carolina, left her mathematics classroom during World War II to work as a "computer" in a radio research laboratory at Harvard University. In 1945 she joined the Naval Research Laboratory (NRL) in Washington, D. C., then reorganizing for post-war projects. Two weeks after she arrived, it was announced that "upper air" research was going to be conducted, using captured German V-2 rockets, the deadly missiles that had terrorized Britain in the closing days of the war.

The V-2 rockets were big and heavy and had to be weighted with lead where their war heads had previously been. For the experiments they were loaded with every kind of scientific experiment imaginable that might help determine the heat, pressure, cosmic rays and other properties of the upper atmosphere, and were shot into the air over the desert at White Sands, New Mexico. Soon it was realized that smaller, more stable rockets were needed, and the family of sounding rockets made its debut: the Aerobee, Spaerobee, Astrobee,

Nike Apache, Nike Cajun, the Javelin, and the Journeyman.

As the sounding rocket program swung into high gear, Eleanor Pressly's job became that of liaison officer between rocket designers, manufacturers, and government and university scientists. For an experiment scheduled to "fly," for instance, she would first discuss its objectives with experimenters, then she would procure the rocket to transport it in. Perhaps she would have a contractor modify its nose-cone, the section where the instrumentation equipment would ride. She might also ask engineers to help her tackle such problems as separating the payload and the rocket so that measurement instruments wouldn't be affected by heat. Finally, dressed in coveralls and a "hard hat," or protective helmet, Miss Pressly would meet with ground crews to co-ordinate the actual launch operations at Wallops Island, Virginia, or at Fort Churchill, Canada.

In 1958 the NRL sounding rocket program was transferred to NASA. That year sixteen sounding rockets were fired. By 1965, Miss Pressly, then desk-bound by her increasing responsibilities, was overseeing the detail connected with firing more than two hundred different kinds of custom-designed experiments each year.

Because sounding rockets are much cheaper to shoot than satellites, scientists, often from colleges and universities, like to use them first to try out new ideas.

49

NASA is receptive to fresh concepts, eager to consult and advise, and, for those experiments that the agency deems worthy to fly, the government will supply all support instrumentation — that is, telemetry, power supply, performance gauges, as well as other kinds of mechanical hardware. Usually, experimenters are interested in aeronomy, biology, energetic particles, magnetic fields, ionospheres, galactic astronomy, solar physics, and the like.

In one experiment, for instance, designed to measure the mysterious atmospheric winds that man needs to know about in order to plan flight paths for spacecraft, sounding rockets release streams of sodium vapor into the upper atmosphere. These rockets are launched at twilight or at dawn when the sunlight is low and the trails can be clearly seen. Pictures are taken of the cloud trails to study their patterns.

In another experiment, winds and temperatures at certain altitudes are measured by ejecting and exploding grenades from a sounding rocket as it descends to earth. In this test, the time and position of the explosions is picked up and recorded by sensitive microphones on the ground. By analyzing this data, the heat and the movement of the atmosphere through which the grenades were popping can be determined.

Dozens of other nations have joined the NASA sounding rocket program. United States and foreign scientists, in collaboration, have collected particles of extraterrestrial dust in the near space region; they have observed what goes on in the upper atmosphere during an eclipse of the sun; and they have launched rockets from the deck of an aircraft carrier off the west coast of South America, near the geomagnetic equator, to find out more about the earth's magnetic field.

New evidence about the universe, its origin and evolution, is being sought also by the astronomers in Dr. Nancy Roman's satellite program. For centuries astronomers have studied the solar system, the stars, nebulae and other celestial objects. Now space technology makes it possible to send orbiting satellites hundreds of miles above the filmy atmosphere that hangs like a veil between earth and the stars. From the satellites astronomical images can be televised back to earth, furnishing valuable information about unknown areas of electromagnetic radiation, the radiation of the stars, and the gases and dust of interstellar space. Soon, man may be able to observe the center of the earth's galaxy, the Milky Way, perhaps even glimpse the edges of the universe.

The director of NASA's astronomy program, Nancy Roman, was always determined to be an astronomer. As a very small child, she saw the beauty of the Northern Lights in Michigan. Then when her family moved to Nevada, where the desert nights were crystal clear and the stars blazed white in the sky, she was so enchanted that she started an astronomy club of friends, who each contributed pennies in order to buy a dime store book that told them about the constellations.

By the time she was twenty-four years old, Nancy Roman had received a Bachelor of Arts degree from Swarthmore College and a Ph.D. from the University of Chicago. Now she was a professional astronomer and astrophysicist. She started immediately to teach and conduct research at the Yerkes Observatory of the University of Chicago, specializing in clusters and stellar populations. After five years, she moved to Washington, D. C., to join radio astronomers at the Naval Research Laboratory (NRL) who were mapping the universe with radio waves and who were soon to turn to something entirely new — measuring the moon by radar.

One winter afternoon in 1959 she drove downtown to hear Dr. Harold Urey, Nobel Prize winner, lecture about the moon. Afterwards, she joined other scientists in group discussion. As usual in those days, the talk turned to space. In particular, the man sitting next to Dr. Roman told her that there was need for a capable astronomer to direct NASA's new astronomy program in which exciting new experiments would be lofted in balloons, sounding rockets, satellites and other spacecraft. Driving home that night Nancy Roman realized that she was being offered the chance to help steer the course of space astronomy. Shortly thereafter she became Head of the Observational Astronomy Program in NASA's Office of Flight Development.

Although early experimental satellites were small and shaped more or less like beach balls, the orbiting observatory satellites now look more like air-borne windmills, flying pencil sharpeners, and soaring beetles. They are made to circle around the earth and are called by such nicknames as OSO, OGO, POGO, EGO, and OAO.

The OGO, or Orbital Geophysical Observatory, helps astronomers to better understand the relationship between the earth and the sun, and the earth's position as a planet. For practical reasons, each OGO is designed to carry many different kinds of experiments and instruments, and to travel in many different kinds of orbits, both close and far away from the earth. In other words, scientists and engineers have modeled a standard vehicle for the skies. OGO satellites, which look like giant dragonflies, will perform a wide variety of complex functions, and in order to contain the necessary experiments and equipment for power, they will eventually be constructed to weigh as much as 1,200 lb.

EGO, the Elliptical Orbiting Geophysical Observatory, in the OGO program, is a satellite that encircles the globe in an eccentric orbit to investigate energetic particles, solar X-Rays, interplanetary dust, and other phenomena in space. EGO satellites will someday carry as many as thirty different but inter-related scientific projects which will simultaneously gather information.

53

POGO, the Polar Orbiting Geophysical Observatory, also in the OGO program, carries experiments to study the atmosphere and ionosphere near earth in the polar regions.

OSO, the Orbiting Solar Observatory, constantly sends back measurements of radiation from the sun; and OAO, the Orbiting Astronomical Observatory, another observational satellite, will give man an undistorted look at the universe above the blanket of the atmosphere.

AOSO, the Advanced Orbiting Solar Observatory, is the "sun tracker"; its purpose is to garner new knowledge of solar energy, without which there would be no life.

Besides administering the expanding satellite program, Dr. Nancy Roman crosses the country to watch over diverse astronomy experiments being tested elsewhere in rockets, balloons, and the X-15 airplane. Unmarried, energetic, she finds time to make her own clothes, cook, weave, teach Sunday School, and trade stamps with astronomers in other countries. But most of the time, she and her colleagues plan ahead for the day when astronomical observatories will be based on the moon or on platforms that fly through the heavens.

CHAPTER

7

THE FIRST UNITED STATES SATELLITE TO ORBIT AROUND the earth was called the Explorer I. Weighing over 30 lb., it was tossed into the sky on January 31, 1958. Circling the world in about two hours, its apogee or furthest point away was 1,587 miles; its perigee or closest point, 219 miles. Delicate but rugged instruments on board the Explorer brought to light unexpected scientific information. It was revealed, for instance, that there was a belt of high-intensity radiation — later called the Van Allen Belt — around the earth.

In only a few years, many dramatic uses for satellites were developed. Some were designed to "hang" in the heavens, to forecast the weather, and to link continents by voice, teletype, and TV. Others were designed to be "deep space probes," the most complex of all unmanned spacecraft, built to escape the earth's gravity and go on missions of discovery millions of miles away.

Year in and year out, day and night, these spacecraft report valuable information about outer space. And electronic engineers, like Marjorie Townsend of the National Aeronautics and Space Administration, keep trying to create more efficient ways to transmit the data to earth.

Mrs. Townsend, mother of four sons, is principally concerned with the instruments that yield scientific information from orbiting weather satellites. Her office is in NASA's Goddard Space Flight Center, an endless maze of modern buildings in Maryland. Specifically, she is the senior electronic engineer who supervised the design of a highly specialized computer that flies on the TIROS and Nimbus meteorological satellites. This computer receives signals from a sensor in the satellites that measures certain temperatures and converts the data into computer language in a format that can be interpreted on the ground.

TIROS (Television Infrared Observation Satellite) is a huge spacecraft shaped like a lady's hat box. Its top and sides are covered with solar cells that continually transform the sun's light into electricity for power. TIROS satellites gather information about the

earth's temperature distribution, and the heights, out-
lines, and temperatures of clouds. This data is then
relayed to tracking stations around the world by
telemeter, a word derived from Greek words meaning
"to measure from afar." Certain systems on board the
TIROS, such as its sensors, recording equipment,
and telemetering equipment, constantly observe the
weather conditions, store the information for a couple
of hours, and transmit it to earth on command as it
passes over ground stations. These tiny electronic systems are planned in Mrs. Townsend's office.

Marjorie Townsend was born and educated in
Washington, D. C. The only daughter of an engineer,
she decided to be an electrical engineer herself when
she was at George Washington University. She was the
first woman graduate from that university in engineering. After college she worked for almost nine years in
anti-submarine warfare research at the Naval Research
Laboratory (NRL) in Washington, D. C. Then in
1959 she joined the space agency.

Her first job at NASA was to build a ground "sta-
tion," a bank of electronic equipment that would filter
and sort out different signals from TIROS for scientists
at Goddard Space Flight Center. Then she and her
team designed the intricate computer that helped turn
certain of these signals into understandable computer
language.

When the first Nimbus, a more advanced meteorological research observatory, was put into orbit in 1964, she helped design the beacon for tracking it and the transmitter on which all data came back to earth. The Nimbus made it possible to take pictures from space of such landmarks as the Volga River in the U.S.S.R., mountain ranges in Sumatra, and the outline of Italy. In the course of fourteen orbits each day, the first Nimbus scanned over seventy per cent of the earth's surface and relayed weather conditions directly to ground stations all over the world. The "weather eyes" of other TIROS and Nimbus satellites will help save agricultural crops and human lives by day to day warnings of storms, hurricanes, typhoons, tornadoes, and other atmospheric disturbances.

Watching over the development of highly advanced transmitters, amplifiers, and oscillators for weather satellites takes much of Marjorie Townsend's time. But she is also responsible for the technical coordination of an ingenious new scientific plan to simulate the earth's atmosphere. Ultimately, this new system will be used to place into orbit a satellite that can keep track of thousands upon thousands of specific, electronically-impregnated objects on earth. The objects might be, for instance, buoys in the sea, balloons in the air, or ships or planes. The satellite's task will be to pick up signals from the objects and then report their location from time to time. For example, signals from a buoy drifting in the sea could help man learn

9. Barbara Short uses miniature models
of spacecraft that are shot out of guns
in order to study aerodynamic stability.

10. Laurel van der Wal Roennau is head of the bioastronautics division of Space Technology Laboratories, Inc. *Space Technology Laboratories, Inc.*

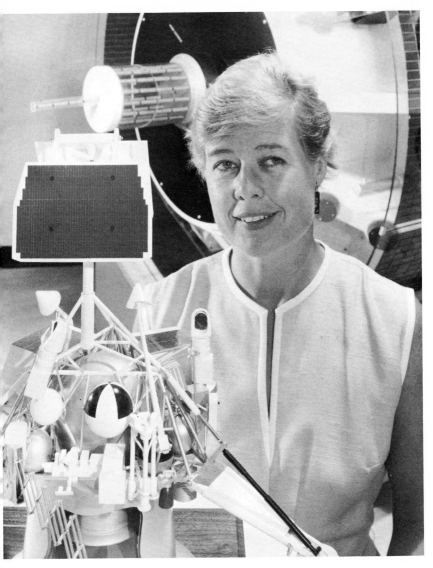

11. Virginia Norwood with a scale model of Surveyor, the unmanned lunar landing space vehicle, and behind her is a mock model of a Syncom.

12. Cheryle C. Smith, an operations research analyst. Here she is giving a presentation on her studies. *Air Force photo, Wright-Patterson AFB, Ohio*

13A. Annette Chambers, who is responsible for the mathematical instructions fed into the computers that guide manned spacecraft into orbit. *Aerospace Corporation*

13B. Marcelline Chartz supervises the writing of computer programs. *NASA photo, Ames Research Center*

14. Margaret Jackson experiencing the
condition of weightlessness. *NASA photo*

15. Dr. Tsu-tzu Tsai, a chemist, seen taking reaction temperatures of synthetic organo tin compounds.
Air Force photo, Wright-Patterson AFB, Ohio

16. Dr. Mildred Mitchell, who works in the new field of bionics. She is working her "nail-bender," an experiment using an artificial muscle. *Bill Garlow,* Journal Herald, *Dayton, Ohio*

more about the path of an ocean current; periodic signals from a balloon floating in the sky could help weather men map air currents more precisely; and animals could be monitored electronically so that the phenomenon of migration could be observed.

The system is called the Interrogation Recording and Location System (IRLS). IRLS satellites will fly in polar orbit, thereby completely covering the natural atmosphere in every area of the world.

The same year that the first weather satellite was launched, the first navigational satellite, Transit, was placed into orbit to guide ships and aircraft with its radio signals. Also that year, Echo I, a huge, silvery, "passive" satellite proved that a world-wide communications network was possible.

Echo was launched on August 12, 1960. That night, millions of Americans clustered together on their front lawns, or climbed out of their automobiles, to watch the star-like object wink steadily across the evening sky. Echo was an inflatable sphere, visible because light was reflected off its thin, aluminum coat, which served as a backboard or mirror for radio signals that were bounced from one point on earth to another.

By 1963, a revolutionary new type of communications satellite demonstrated even more dramatically that outer space could be used for peaceful, useful purposes. A family of Syncom satellites, named for "synchronous communications satellite," was developed and built by scientists at Hughes Aircraft Company, a highly secret defense and space plant that sprawls over acres of hills on the lip of the Los Angeles basin. High in its management planning is Virginia Norwood, an engineer.

Mrs. Norwood is primarily concerned with research in the "microwave region," that area of the radio spectrum between approximately 1,000 megacycles and 300,000 megacycles. On the first Syncom, her research was important in the development of its microwave antenna. The miniature parts she worked with look like bright bits of candy wrapped in colored paper, but they are the life force of the shiny, black communications satellite which, traveling approximately 6,875 miles per hour at an altitude of 22,300 miles, matches the speed of the earth's rotation and appears to stand still or "hang" in space.

A Syncom is used for communications as if it were a relay tower thousands of miles high. Two Syncoms parked in space can now transmit at the same time by microwave-relay thousands of telephone, telegraph, and teletype messages, and television and wire photo service to nearly two-thirds of the world. A third Syncom will provide these services from any area in the entire world to any area of the world, except for isolated regions near the North and South Poles.

Virginia Norwood, the daughter of an Army engineer, always had a special interest in machine shops and pure mathematics. Her school teachers, in particular, provided definite direction for her life. In the eighth grade, she learned to measure building heights by means of shadows and homemade transits; she also learned to like algebra from experimenting with puzzles. In the tenth grade, she was taught to see the possible interrelation of such subjects as trigonometry, chemistry, and physics. Then in her sophomore year at the Massachusetts Institute of Technology, where she earned her B.S. degree in mathematical physics, she married her calculus professor.

The Norwoods, who were for several years a scientific "package team," joined Hughes Aircraft Company together in 1954. Mrs. Norwood became Head of the Microwaves Group. Her analyses and experiments with micrawave antennae were done both in machine shops and in laboratories where the tiny components were tested on what is called a "bread board." When the doll-sized circuits were spread out on bread boards, breakdowns, leaks, and jam-ups could be more easily perceived; later, when the systems were corrected and perfected the same circuits were fitted together compactly inside the satellite.

Because she was experienced and knowledgeable in communications research and development, Mrs. Norwood was selected for membership in the Hughes "advance planning" group. These are the scientist-administrators who evaluate new plans for spacecraft.

61

They work by gathering together what they call a "bull-pen" team which examines and discusses ideas. To be a member, one must have a fertile imagination. And often, because the industry is highly competitive, Virginia Norwood finds herself a member of a team that is working a seventy-hour week.

The Ranger program was a series of space probes that eventually yielded over 17,000 close-up pictures of the pitted face of the moon, though initially, Ranger probes failed to accomplish their complicated goals. On July 31, 1964, Ranger VII hurtled for three days toward the moon, and then, precisely on schedule, at twenty-five minutes and forty-nine seconds after nine, turned on one of its six cameras, filmed the equatorial region of the moon, and crashed into its side. Ground antennae at Goldstone, California, Woomera, Australia, and Johannesburg, South Africa, received the radio waves from space and converted them into pictures that showed a landscape comprised of odd shaped craters, foamy fissures, "rills," and strange, rock-like masses. *The New York Times* summed up the feat by saying, "Ranger VII obtained and transmitted to the earth more detailed information about the moon than man has ever had before."

Ranger barely prepared the world for the subsequent triumphs conceived and carried out by scientists: the Mariner missions. On December 14, 1962, a

Mariner flew to Venus and sent back news about the planet's surface temperature showing it to be about 800 degrees Fahrenheit and —30 to —70 degrees at the tops of the clouds surrounding the planet. In addition, important information about interplanetary spaces was recorded.

But the Mariner flight that will be most remembered was climaxed on July 14, 1965, when cameras 135 million miles away swept across the surface of Mars and sent back to earth a stream of "binary digest," a special computer language, from which it was possible to actually reconstruct pictures of the surface of our sister planet.

The Mars Mariner was stuffed with tiny electronic instruments that sent back information from a variety of space experiments that were conducted on the long, 228 day space flight. Among other discoveries, scientists learned that the physical features of Mars are more like the moon than the earth, that the density of its air is thin; and that it is perhaps two to five billion years old. Most important of all, the Mariner gave new clues to the evolution of the solar system and strongly suggested that the earth is more unique than it was previously considered to be.

Planning spacecraft systems such as these means that scientists must incorporate the latest and most applicable theories about space into plans for craft that will not fly for several years. Take, for example, the

Pegasus. This is a huge, scientific "space bird" that will unfold thin aluminum foil wings ninety-six feet long. Each time bits of space debris from meteoroids, asteroids, or comets hit the wing skin they will be "counted up" by an electrical charge. Pegasus data about this rain of matter, which is produced when celestial bodies break up, will enable engineers to construct safer, puncture-proof spacecraft.

Other knowledge will be garnered from a "moon bus" called the Surveyor. It is designed to land gently on the moon. There it will sample the lunar soil by drilling into it, chewing it up, and televising an analysis. A ten-watt transmitter, designed by Virginia Norwood's team, will send the television pictures from the moon to earth. From them engineers will gain the understanding they need of the moon's surface so that they can build safe landing gear for the spacecraft carrying men.

Biosatellites, carrying wheat shoots, fruit flies, bread mold, fertilized frogs' eggs and other live organisms, will be tested in space for varying periods of time to see how different types of life adjust. Some biosatellites may carry "sticky string," a device coated with an adhesive mixture, to trap any microbes that might exist on other planets. Findings from these kinds of experiments will have to be correlated carefully before man dares step into new worlds that may be hostile or dangerous.

CHAPTER

8

WHEN A SPACE CAPSULE, SATELLITE, OR SPACE PROBE
lifts from its launch pad and severs its ties to earth, it
carries within it intelligence in the form of a man-made
brain, the computer. At the same time, on the ground,
an intricate network of computers in control centers and
tracking stations all over the world, chews up and spits
out critical mathematical equations that control and
guide the craft. Without these high speed machines,
which are capable of being "programmed" to transmit
and store data and to both give and receive orders,
there could not be a space program as we know it today.

Women seem particularly suited for working with
computers. In fact, Ada Augusta, Countess of Lovelace,
daughter of the poet Byron, may have been the first

woman "programmer" — one who prepares, simplifies, and translates a problem and the data bearing on it into an electronic language that a computer can handle. She was a brilliant mathematician, who wrote lucid accounts of the concept of a remarkable "analytical engine" invented in about 1815 by her eccentric colleague, Charles Babbage. Babbage's contraption was the first scientific computer. It employed basically the same principles as the ancient abacus and presaged today's space-age computers, which are capable of calculating thousands of computations each second.

With data from computers, scientists can determine the distance of a spacecraft from the earth or the sun or the moon and correlate this information in such a way as to establish and maintain precise trajectories, or flight paths. Moreover, unknown forces exerting pressures on the craft can be studied. And, since 1958, when the hunch of a mathematician gave scientists a new concept of the shape of the earth, tracking data has been used to help determine the exact dimensions of the earth's mass.

The mathematician was Ann Eckels Bailie, who was tracking the second United States satellite, Vanguard I. In its early days, it was Mrs. Bailie's job to put into equations and onto graphs the data it transmitted by radio waves to computers in tracking stations.

In checking this information, Mrs. Bailie and the

group of mathematicians and astronomers who were working at the same thing, noticed that the perigee of the Vanguard orbit — its nearest point to earth — was different for the northern hemisphere than for the southern hemisphere. This was totally unexpected information and led them to speculate that somehow mathematical errors were being made.

Shortly afterward, flying back to Washington from a scientific meeting in Boston, Mrs. Bailie had occasion to reconsider. She was seated beside the assistant chief of her division, Dr. John A. O'Keefe, who had in his hand a round lump of Silly Putty — a commercial synthetic clay — which prompted the couple to start discussing the shape of the earth and its tendency to spread or bulge slightly at the equator. Mrs. Bailie told him about the peculiar orbital data from Vanguard, and as they talked suddenly it occurred to them both that the unexpected variations in Vanguard's orbital behavior might not be due to a man-made mistake, but to the gravitational pull of the earth, different in the northern hemisphere than the southern. After analysis of this theory, scientists eventually endorsed the concept that the earth is asymmetrical, shaped like a fat pear, with the stem pointing northward.

At about the same time that Mrs. Bailie was tracking Vanguard, another young mathematical analyst was using data from computers to help keep track of the big ballistic missiles that were being shot from Cape Kennedy. Helen Mann was plotting and predicting where the missiles would land if their engines were cut off at a given moment. This is vital information for an astronaut because his spacecraft might have to be brought back to earth before achieving its planned number of orbits in space.

When missile testing first started, Mrs. Mann was usually the only woman at the Cape in AZUSA, the Impact Predictor Building. During those times it was up to her to signal the range safety officer to "destruct" or to destroy a missile if the computers indicated that it was starting to go astray. In addition, to "down range" radar tracking stations, located on southern islands in the Atlantic, Mrs. Mann teletyped a steady stream of computations regarding the horizontal direction or bearing, elevation, and range of the missile in flight, thereby keeping island inhabitants, stray fishermen, and crews on recovery ships informed of just where a missile would land.

Because of her skill in developing computer programs for impact prediction, and her understanding of engineering data from missiles, Helen Mann was picked to help a group of engineers design the efficient, economical computation facility that is now a part of the Atlantic Missile Range.

In all of the major space programs, there are

women working with data systems who turn raw research into important reports for the use of scientists and engineers. Mrs. Mary Hedgepeth, for instance, the wife of an aircraft radar and optical tracking specialist and mother of two sons, heads a large section of mathematical data analysts at Edwards Air Force Base, California. This is the 300,000-acre Air Force Flight Test Center in the Mojave Desert where experimental research aircraft such as the X-15 are flown far into outer space to test new fuels, structural fatigue, and to solve aerodynamic problems.

In preparation for test flights, Mrs. Hedgepeth's group analyzes previous flight data relevant to velocity, acceleration, flight path, and air position of the craft. Many problems that might affect future flights are solved here by turning this data into a numerical and alphabetical language for computer use.

Annette Chambers uses computer data in a different way. Her office is in the Aerospace Corporation in El Segundo, California. During manned space-launches, however, she can be found working with a multi-million dollar bank of guidance computers at Cape Kennedy, Florida.

Mrs. Chambers is called a guidance project engineer. She is responsible for the mathematical instructions that are fed into the computers that guide manned spacecraft into proper orbit. The lives of the astronauts depend on accurate mathematical computations as well as faultless operation of the computers and their switches.

When basic research scientists can solve their highly experimental problems on computers their work is facilitated and new discoveries come through more quickly. To make it possible for new kinds of problems to be solved on computers, Marcelline Chartz at NASA's Ames Research Center at Moffett Field, has been trying for years to improve the efficiency of computing machines. A native of San Francisco, she has operated, wired, repaired, and programmed computers, and now supervises the writing of programs that constantly spin out algebraic answers to basic research problems of all types. It is her job to maintain a truly creative staff of programmers who can assist the Ames scientists who are asking new kinds of questions and need accurate answers in the fastest, most direct way.

On the other hand, Nan Glennon uses her understanding of computer capability to streamline space plant management problems. She works at Thompson Ramo Woolridge, Inc. (TRW) and co-ordinates staggering quantities of data about every phase in the development of spacecraft: the design on the drafting board, the model on the assembly line, and the finished product.

A comical, lucky mistake when she was at the University of Southern California set the course of Miss Glennon's life. Enrolling in a "mechanics" course, which she thought would help her to understand what was under the hood of her old jalopy, she found out that it was instead a physics course for engineers. She stayed for the lecture, decided to become a mechanical engineer, and in only four years completed a five year engineering program to become the first woman graduate in the department of engineering at USC.

At nineteen she went to work in one of the Standard Oil Company's refineries, building boilers, and designing high-pressure steam systems, gasoline-treating plant utilities, and sewer installations. But after realizing that her real talent seemed to be in making things mesh, or in "systems engineering," she joined the space industry, hoping to become an administrator.

At Space Technology Laboratories, which was later to become TRW, Inc., she was assigned to a special program for analyzing proposals, sales leads, and contracts on computers. But first she had to learn to be a programmer.

"Like a recipe, a program for a computer is just a series of simple steps," she said, explaining the art she has now mastered. "It is like learning to fry an egg. You have to take it step by step. One: open the cupboard door. Two: take out the flat pan. Three: lay the pan on the stove. And so on through the butter and egg routine."

Miss Glennon quickly became adept at dovetailing business transactions. She was then chosen to be on the team responsible for the first Transit-Courier space satellite. This was the first rocket built to coast, restart in space, and shove into orbit the first navigational satellite. She scheduled all operations, from design through fabrication, development testing, assembly, and launch. With creative use of the computers, she was able to keep track of the extremely complex project.

Now Miss Glennon's type of work is being duplicated in most aerospace industries, where scientists, engineers, and administrators turn to computers almost as if they were human colleagues. In fact, without this assistance it would be utterly impossible to keep developing new plans or to sift through the unprecedented quantity of detail that has already been spawned since the advent of the space age.

CHAPTER

9

ALTHOUGH DECADES MAY PASS BEFORE HUMAN BEINGS will actually send colonies to the hostile environments of other planets, scientists and engineers are already planning space trips for mechanical men who will be able to rationalize, smell, thread a needle, and even reproduce themselves. These robots will perform some of the functions of an astronaut: they will land on strange surfaces, collect and process the information that they find there, and if possible, avoid dangerous, unforeseen obstacles in the process. The technical knowledge for creating these man-made men will be gained from studying a variety of living organisms such as stink bugs, rats, and elephant trunks. This is the extraordinary new science called "bionics."

Some say the word bionics was coined from *"bi*ology" and "electr*onics"*; others point out that the term means "lifelike" in Greek. Mildred Mitchell, a bionicist in the Air Force Avionics Laboratory at Wright-Patterson Air Force Base in Dayton, Ohio, explains it this way: "Bionics is an interdisciplinary science that creates things that behave like living organisms. In other words, it is a new science in which psychologists, biologists, physicians, chemists, physicists, mathematicians, and engineers team together to electronically duplicate the functions of men, animals, and plants."

Man has been copying nature for centuries. The cave dweller who wrapped himself in animal skins to keep warm was applying the principles of bionics. Indian warriors who learned to camouflage their bodies by studying the protective markings of animals were bionicists of sorts. So were airplane designers who patterned their crafts after birds.

Scientists today are using bionic precepts as they study bats in order to learn more about radar. The bat's brain, weighing only a fraction of an ounce, contains better antennae than the best that man has been able to produce. Study may help man to duplicate it for his own uses. Similarly, studying porpoises in the sea may help improve sonar for submarines.

The above are evident uses of bionics, but the astonishing electronic space machines built in Dr.

Mildred Mitchell's laboratory almost defy the imagination. Take for example the "artificial muscle," a mechanical model of the muscle in a man's body. Its purpose is to aid a space pilot who is encountering the stresses of take-off and landing under high G's, at which time it is impossible for him to lift his arm to manipulate necessary controls; the muscle may also assist an astronaut who has experienced long periods of weightlessness, during which his muscles could become weak or impaired.

The muscle substitutes are light-weight. They are composed of about 130,000 inelastic fibers imbedded in a tube of material. Molded together, the fibers look like a thin stalk of celery. These muscles can lift very heavy objects for short distances with a high degree of efficiency. In a little contraption that Dr. Mitchell calls a "nail bender," an artificial muscle bends a hefty nail easily with a tiny puff of air.

Another ingenious bionics device may make it possible to move man-made muscles by merely *trying*. In other words, the electrical "potential," or nerve impulse from the brain, may be picked up by electrodes, amplified, and sent to an artificial muscle. Thus the electronic aid may raise a man's arm if he just wills it.

The "biological clock" is a good example of the way that biology can be applied to "hardware," the space word for equipment. Under Dr. Mitchell's direction, engineers analyzed data obtained from desert rodents, who stay underground all day but come out to feed at night. When kept in continuous darkness, the rats became active at about the same time they would ordinarily go out for dinner each evening. But when the periods of light and dark — and heat and cold — were shifted around, the animals soon changed their habits and adjusted. An electronic machine, called the "biological clock," was then created to imitate the way the rats acted in surroundings that constantly changed. Eventually, using this concept, spacecraft may be built with instruments that automatically adjust to the heat and light of strange environments.

The animal sensory processes offer a wealth of possible models for bionicists. For example, a synthetic retina of a frog's eye, built to conform to data obtained from experiments on live frogs, has been built into space equipment so it will scan the face of other planets. And studies of human perception are being conducted in order to build electronic brains that will help spacecraft avoid crash landings on other celestial bodies.

Man's sense of touch is also being simulated. For example, during those times when the noise of blast-off or the stresses of high-G's or weightlessness prevent a pilot from receiving important signals, a means of communicating orders to him through his skin nerves is being refined — something like the Braille reading system for the blind. Tiny jets of air from miniature electronic equipment built into his space suit will stimulate him to action. Called tactile control, it is both effective and agreeable. Eventually, when more of man's sensory processes can be duplicated, "mechanical men" will be built to supplement the work of the astronaut.

Bionics research will also have applications for man on earth. Muscle substitutes will benefit the physically handicapped. Studies of the ears of birds may help us to discover what sounds will drive them away; then science can duplicate these sounds, electronically, in order to drive birds away from airports where crashes are caused when they are sucked into jet plane engines. Similarly, the sounds that insects dislike may be copied to help save crops by driving bugs away from fields of grain or groves of fruit trees.

Planning and building bionics equipment requires a special ability to apply unlimited imagination to very practical things. Another prerequisite is knowledge and skill in a variety of fields. Mildred Mitchell, for example, has degrees in mathematics, philosophy, and psychology; she has been a schoolteacher, college professor, hospital psychologist; she studied hypnosis, traveled widely, and specialized in dramatics.

Her involvement in space began long before bionics became a science. In 1958, she joined the Aerospace Medical Research Laboratory at Wright-Patterson Air

77

Force Base in Dayton, Ohio, to conduct psychological tests on men in isolation. Scientists needed to know, for example, if men would have wild nightmares on long, long flights to the moon. Would they forget what time it was and ignore important signals from the ground? Would they be driven to insanity from loneliness?

By locking men up in the dark. Dr. Mitchell found that some subjects became agitated, unreasonable, furious, and demanded release. Others fell asleep, and denied that they had. One man dozed for forty-two minutes, but swore it was only six. Many volunteers left the isolation chamber before their time was up. (But one stubborn woman stuck it out for seven days.)

When the seven original Project Mercury astronauts were to be chosen, Dr. Mitchell was asked to serve on the panel of experts that evaluated candidates. "In selecting the first seven astronauts we were handicapped because we could not observe other men doing the job," she said. "At that time, no men had been shot into space, so we did the next best thing. We studied men who had flown higher and faster than other men in testing new aircraft.

"We asked ourselves over and over: what happens to a man when he is put under physical stress? Does he 'blackout,' quit, or continue on the job?

"The answer lies not only in the physical reaction of his body, but in his motivation and emotional ma-

78

turity." Looking back, Dr. Mitchell points with pride to the mature men chosen to participate in the nation's first flights into space.

In 1960, when it became clear that the problems of extended space flight were too far from solution, the risk to human life too great, and that electronic equipment that behaved like living organisms might first prepare the way, Dr. Mitchell pitched into her unusual bionics program. In only a short time she and other inventive scientists in government and private industry, working together in teams, have turned thoughts of pure fiction into realistic laboratory machines for the benefit of man.

CHAPTER

10

WOMEN SCIENTISTS AND ENGINEERS ARE RECEIVING MORE and more recognition for their efforts to enrich space science. Less often publicized, however, are the thousands of other women with almost indispensable supporting jobs. These are the back-up members of America's space team, whose skills and aptitudes are applied to all phases of the many programs to explore the universe.

Miss Ida Young is a good example. She is a talented oil painter; but her space career revolves around the editing of technical space reports. Miss Young edited John Glenn's account of the first United States manned orbital mission. Quite obviously, reports of this nature are invaluable for space engineers — and for posterity.

Dorothy Morris is a research librarian at the Lewis Research Center in Cleveland, Ohio. Her work at this NASA installation entails processing literally tons of important technical reference materials about space so that it will be quickly accessible to busy scientists.

Helping to interpret our progress in space to the public is often a job held by a woman. Mrs. Mary Louise Gosney at Lewis Research Center and Grace Kennedy Winn at Houston's Manned Space Flight Center arrange tours of their facilities for the press and visiting dignitaries. Mrs. Gosney also sets up interviews with space scientists, and arranges meals and housing for them. And Mrs. Winn's duties involve community relations with schools and civic groups.

Dorothy Whidden is an artist who illustrates reports and pamphlets describing new space experiments. Located at Lewis Research Center, she is called upon to draw ideas that depict concepts not easily explained in words.

In another field entirely, Mrs. Carmonelle Pinkston, in the Aeronautical Systems Division at Wright-Patterson Air Force Base, is the chief of the "classification and wage branch" of civilian personnel. Mrs. Pinkston and her staff analyze the difficulties and scopes of aerospace jobs and establish proper pay for each position.

"There is hardly a profession that doesn't contribute to America's current space program. And imaginative, capable women will always be needed badly, no matter how varied their vocational interests may be." These are the words of Laurel van der Wal Roennau, an enthusiastic pioneer space scientist who is also a wife, a mother of two sons, and an important begetter of space ideas.

Mrs. Roennau was one of the first young women to join industry in space research. As a member of the research and development division of the Space Technology Laboratories, Inc., now known as TRW, Inc., she quickly became head of its "bioastronautic" division. In this capacity she originated Project MIA (Mouse in Able), a program in which the heart beats of white mice, cradled in the nose-cones of rockets, were telemetered back to earth. These were the very first high altitude animal experiments in weightlessness.

Other experiments in weightlessness that she conducted concerned the interaction of gases and liquids in zero G; scientists had to know, for instance, if water in space would crawl up the side of a glass, form a globule, or an emulsion. Tests to decide these things were sent up in early rockets.

Now Mrs. Roennau plans for the day when space-craft that can take off and land, straight up and down, at speeds of up to 8,000 miles per hour will be used by the public. In fact, ideas for building "spaceports" to house these hypersonic planes with vertical flight capability have been discussed in her office already. She also serves on a space advisory committee whose function is to apply space technology to civic problems such as jet noise, traffic control, parking, urban renewal, medical records, and so on.

Not only is our concept of flying changing in dramatic ways but, like Columbus, who was searching for the spices and riches of the Indies when he found the New World quite by accident, man continues to stumble upon great discoveries when he is really looking for something else. And since the dawn of the space age, our way of life has been enhanced, and the nation's economy has been revitalized, by daily, unexpected discoveries or by the by-products of space research, otherwise known as "spin-off," "fall-out," "peel-off," or "pay-off."

The new materials invented so that spacecraft can withstand stresses, strains, and violent changes of temperature, for example, have given rise to new lines of building materials and plastic housewares. Concentrated freeze-dried foods, delicious, economical, and convenient, first tested on space-bound pilots, have been introduced into daily use.

Soon there will be person-to-person communications, with both sound and picture, any place on earth. And satellites, built for exploring space, will serve as around-the-clock fire-watchers, flood-watchers, and guardians against other natural catastrophes that might endanger people on airplanes and ships, on farms and in mountains — even on teams engaged in outdoor sports.

In medicine and health, particularly, space research discoveries will continue to uplift and sustain mankind. Sensing and measuring devices, developed for satellites, are revolutionizing diagnostic techniques. Electronic sensors, like those taped to the bodies of astronauts to measure their physical reactions, are being used for hospital patients to signal warnings of changes in their condition. Cryogenic, or deep cold, surgery has been improved from research on low-temperature liquids for use in space. Soon there will be mechanical muscles for paraplegics, developed from bionics research; toothpaste that can be swallowed; and hospitals in orbit around the earth where pregnant women and heart patients will be safer because their bodies will not have to struggle against the pull of gravity.

Such a fine rich future will call for the energies of both men and women with varying talents and gifts. They will be needed to work for long hours. They will meet delay and disappointment. For brief periods of time, their personal lives may suffer. But by the very nature of their work in space, a thread of fantasy will run through their lives, reminding them that their goal has been man's dream throughout the ages.

Index of women and fields of work

Numbers in italic refer to illustrations:
1-8 follow page 26; *9-16* follow page 58

Since 1957 MARY FINCH HOYT has specialized in writing and editing material about government and military activities. At the present time she is a senior staff member for the Historical Evaluation and Research Organization in Washington. Here she participates in staff studies prepared for general and specific use.

Mrs. Hoyt was born in Visalia, California, and was educated at San Jose State College, the University of California at Los Angeles and American University in Washington. She is the mother of two sons, Thomas Wade Hoyt and Stephen Mitchell Hoyt.